CONTEMPORARY CLOZE

Written by George Moore

PRIM-ED PUBLISHING
www.prim-ed.com

Titles in this series:

LOWER (Ages 5–7)

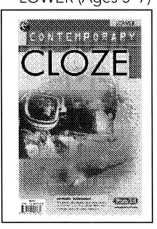

0661

MIDDLE (Ages 7-9)

0662

UPPER (Ages 9–11)

0663

Foreword

Cloze *is an effective teaching strategy widely used to assist in the development of reading and comprehension skills. Semantic and syntactic skills are developed as pupils use the context clues around the missing words in the text to make sense of each individual sentence.*

As the title suggests, Contemporary Cloze – Middle *covers a wide range of contemporary topics. These include up-to-date information about popular interests or themes, recent inventions or developments, and discussion about a selection of contemporary issues.*

A variety of learning areas is covered including science, geography, technology, the arts, PSHE and physical education.

Other titles in this series: Contemporary Cloze –Lower (Ages 5–7)
                                                    Contemporary Cloze – Upper (Ages 11+)

The author wishes to thank his wife, Mary Moore, for her assistance during the writing of this book.

Contents

Teachers Notes .... ii – iii
Curriculum Links iv
Bicycles! Bicycles! Bicycles! 1
Raising Healthy Children (**Verbs**) 2
Strange Creatures.. 3
Sun Safety 4
Animated Films (**Verbs**) 5
Children's Toys 6
Graffiti 7
Dinosaurs 8
Homes of the Future.. 9
Patterns and Numbers in Nature (**Nouns**) 10
Speed! (**Nouns**)... 11
Games Around the World 12
Fighting Malaria... 13
Nature Fights Back.. 14
Space Travel (**Adjectives**) 15
Our Changing Language 16
Computers and Your Health (**Adjectives**) 17
Benefits from Space Research (**Nouns**) 18
The Book or the Film? 19
Endangered Animal Snippets 20
The Water Cycle 21
Multicultural Foods 22
The Harry Potter Phenomenon (**Nouns**)................................... 23
Antarctica 24
Astronauts 25
Answers .... 26 – 27

Teachers Notes

Contemporary Cloze provides pupils with the opportunity to practise using semantic and syntactic skills to assist in the development of reading and comprehension. Pupils use the context clues around the missing words in the text to make sense of individual sentences.

A variety of contemporary topics is covered including popular pupil interests or themes, recent inventions or developments, or discussion about a contemporary issue.

In some activities, pupils are provided with the list of missing words. After reading the text, pupils should sort out the obvious choices first and cross out the words as they are used.

Sometimes pupils will need to refer to a map, diagram or illustration to work out the missing word.

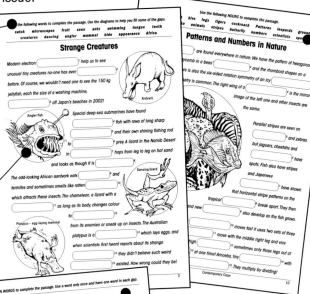

The missing words may be a random selection or a specific group of words such as nouns, verbs or adjectives.

In other activities, pupils must choose their own words to complete the text. Again, pupils should sort out the obvious choices first. Pupils may choose different words to the answers provided. These may still be correct if used in the proper context.

Further suggestions:

- The topic can be discussed with the whole class or in small groups before pupils complete the cloze activity.
- Some of the contemporary topics suggest further discussion following the completion of the activity. Reports by small research groups on particular topics could feature in a series of lessons.
- Unless teachers want to assess the ability of individual pupils, the cloze activities could be completed in pairs to enable an interchange of ideas. This works well with less capable readers, who could be partnered with a reader of the same ability or learn from a more capable pupil.
- Similarly, the activities could be enlarged and completed as a group or class. The teacher could model techniques to work out the missing words.
- Encourage the use of dictionaries to clarify the meaning of difficult words.
- Teachers could revise with the pupils a particular part of speech for the activities where a specific group of words is missing. These include:

  Nouns   are naming words like 'dog', 'Africa', 'summer'.

  Adjectives   are words which describe nouns or words which represent nouns (pronouns). Adjectives usually appear in front of the word they describe but can appear after that word: e.g. 'The boy is tall'.

  Verbs   used are mainly 'action' words; e.g. 'run', 'fly', 'skate' etc.

Teachers Notes

Relevant background information has been included where necessary for each topic.

Graffiti .... *Page 7*
- In the early days, graffiti was mainly used by street gangs and political activists wanting to get their messages to the public.

Dinosaurs .... *Page 8*
- A person who is an expert on prehistoric life through the study of fossils is a palaeontologist.

Patterns and Numbers in Nature .... *Page 10*
- A growing amoeba divides into a pair of smaller cells, each one a new amoeba. So amoebas multiply by dividing!

Games Around the World .... *Page 12*
- The class could be split into small groups to play the games listed. They could then rotate round the games during the lesson(s).
- Haba Gaba: African children may have used nuts, rocks etc., but beanbags or rolled-up socks can be used.

Nature Fights Back .... *Page 14*
- Fire ants in America and Australia are believed to have been imported accidentally in ships' cargoes.

Our Changing Language .... *Page 16*
- See how many shortened words the class can find—a group competition?

Benefits from Space Research .... *Page 18*
- The infrared sensors react to the heat given off by objects like pottery, which stand out as three-dimensional images.
- Shuttles have to withstand high temperatures (up to 1600°C) caused by friction as they re-enter the Earth's atmosphere.
- NASA – National Aeronautics and Space Administration.

The Water Cycle .... *Page 21*
- When air cools it contracts. This brings water droplets in clouds closer together to form larger drops as they touch. These larger drops are heavier and can't be held up by the air currents in clouds so they fall as rain.
- Wet a patch on the blackboard. Wait for a while and it disappears, which shows evaporation has occurred.

The Harry Potter Phenomenon .... *Page 23*
- *The Little White Horse* was written by Elizabeth Goudge and was the Carnegie Medal-winning book in 1946.

Astronauts .... *Page 25*
- Radiation storms are bursts of electrically charged cosmic rays which travel through space at almost the speed of light. The radiation belts around Jupiter are much stronger than those around Earth and pose a threat to any space exploration.
- Gravity: Microgravity is a greatly reduced pull of gravity, whereas zero gravity is weightlessness in space.

Curriculum Links

The activities within the three-book series *Contemporary Cloze* have been written to assist the development of reading and comprehension skills. The non-fiction cloze activities encourage pupils to use a range of strategies to make sense of what they read, thus helping to develop their ability to read with fluency, accuracy, understanding and enjoyment.

The activities in *Contemporary Cloze* demonstrate the following objectives of the Reading Programme of Study of the English National Curriculum.

Book	Year	English Programme of Study		
Lower	1 and 2	Reading	Pupils should be taught:	
			1.k	to work out the sense of a sentence by rereading or reading ahead
			1.l	to focus on meaning derived from the text
			5	knowledge, skills and understanding through a range of non-fiction texts
Middle	3 and 4	Reading	Pupils should be taught:	
			1.c	to use knowledge of grammatical structures
			1.d	to use contextual understanding
			7	knowledge, skills and understanding through a range of non-fiction texts
Upper	5 and 6	Reading	Pupils should be taught:	
			1.c	to use knowledge of grammatical structures
			1.d	to use contextual understanding
			7	knowledge, skills and understanding through a range of non-fiction texts

Use the following words to complete the letter. You will need to read the graph to fill some of the spaces.

accidents   Japan   school   copied   gifts   America   roads   year

crowded   holiday   cars   popular   factories   barriers   three

Bicycles! Bicycles! Bicycles!

Guilin Cottages,
5 March

Dear Roslyn,

I'm enjoying our ⬜¹ travelling

around China but I've never seen so many bicycles! This

Approximate Number of Bicycles in Year 2003

	Millions
India	45
Holland	11
America	103
Mexico	12
China	300
Japan	60

country has ⬜² hundred million, about three times the number in

⬜³ and five times as many as ⬜⁴. I bet when bikes

were invented over 150 years ago they didn't realise they would be so

⬜⁵. In China, a bicycle has usually been one

of the wedding ⬜⁶ a groom gives his bride!

Bicycles are used for local travel such as going to

⬜⁷ or to work. Millions jam the streets of

cities and many cyclists die in road ⬜⁸ because they swerve in and out

of traffic. To encourage people to use old, ⬜⁹ public buses, Beijing,

China's capital, has banned bikes from busy ⬜¹⁰ between 7.00 a.m. and

8.00 a.m. They're also removing protective ⬜¹¹ or trees which separate

car lanes from bicycles. Guangzhou has banned ⬜¹² over 15 years old

and motorcycles from its city centre. That means more bikes!

Next week we go to Shanghai where ⬜¹³ produce over four million

bicycles every ⬜¹⁴. Let's hope there's a subway!

Your friend, Jane.

P.S. I ⬜¹⁵ the graph from a magazine.

Use the following VERBS to complete the passage.

Keep   warned   means   choose   wash   showed   improves   spend
doubled   include   helps   work   visit   builds   stay

Raising Healthy Children

Many children in developed countries [_____]¹ too much time in front of TV or computer screens. The drop in physical exercise [_____]² 10% of British children are obese, a rate which has [_____]³ in the last twenty years! Regular exercise is important as it [_____]⁴ to prevent weight problems and [_____]⁵ the work done by the heart and lungs.

For decades, American doctors have [_____]⁶ parents about high levels of fat and sugar in 'junk' foods. Research in 2002 [_____]⁷ Americans still spend around $200 billion on fast food each year, with over 300 companies to [_____]⁸ from! The high fat content in 'junk' foods means the body has to [_____]⁹ much harder to digest it. A child's diet should [_____]¹⁰ plenty of vegetables, cereals and fruit. [_____]¹¹ fried chips, cakes, ice-cream etc. for special occasions. Your body constantly [_____]¹² new cells so your skin, brain, muscles and bones come from the same source—food.

As well as diet and exercise, there are some other simple steps to [_____]¹³ healthy. Don't carry heavy school bags, which can lead to neck and back problems, take care in the sun and always [_____]¹⁴ your hands after you [_____]¹⁵ the toilet. Good health is so important as you grow up.

Use the following words to complete the passage. Use the diagrams to help you fill some of the gaps.

catch   microscopes   fruit   seen   ants   swimming   tongue   teeth
creatures   dancing   angler   mammal   hide   appearance   Africa

Strange Creatures

Modern electron [_____]¹ help us to see

unusual tiny creatures no-one has ever [_____]²

before. Of course, we wouldn't have needed one to see the

150 kg jellyfish, each the size of a washing machine,

[_____]³ off Japan's beaches in 2002!

Aardvark
– anteater

Angler fish

Special deep-sea submarines have found

[_____]⁴ fish with rows of long sharp

[_____]⁵ and their own shining fishing rod

to [_____]⁶ prey. A lizard in the Namib Desert

in [_____]⁷ hops from leg to leg on hot sand

and looks as though it is [_____]⁸.

The odd-looking African aardvark eats [_____]⁹ and

termites and sometimes smells like rotten [_____]¹⁰,

which attracts these insects. The chameleon, a lizard with a

[_____]¹¹ as long as its body, changes colour

to [_____]¹²

African
dancing
lizard

from its enemies or sneak up on insects. The Australian

platypus is a [_____]¹³ which lays eggs, and

when scientists first heard reports about its strange

[_____]¹⁴ they didn't believe such weird

[_____]¹⁵ existed. How wrong could they be!

Platypus – egg-laying mammal

Use the following words to complete the poem. This poem is made up of rhyming couplets, which means two lines following each other rhyme (aa, bb, cc and so on). Knowing that the words rhyme at the ends of each line pair should help you.

| plus | aware | thin | delay | school | fuss | sex |
| rule | play | grey | checks | tan | skin | midday | can |

Sun Safety

Many admire a dark brown [_____]¹,

But it's best to avoid it if you [_____]².

The ozone layer is now so [_____]³,

It increases the danger to your [_____]⁴.

In the summer heat just don't [_____]⁵,

Especially when you're out at [_____]⁶.

Use a sunscreen, '15 [_____]⁷',

And put on a hat without any [_____]⁸.

Teachers protect the pupils at [_____]⁹,

'No hat, no play!' is a common [_____]¹⁰.

Avoid that sun around [_____]¹¹,

And even take care when the skies are [_____]¹².

Visit the doctor for regular [_____]¹³,

Cancer is a problem for either [_____]¹⁴.

People long ago just weren't [_____]¹⁵,

Our 21st century message 'YOU MUST TAKE CARE!'

Use the following VERBS to complete the passage.

painted   gallops   records   drawn   take   displayed   checks   use
complete   jump   began   paid   placed   mixed   move

Animated Films

Animation perhaps _____¹ when our early ancestors drew animals galloping

across cave walls or ancient Egyptians _____² pictures inside tombs and

temples.

To produce an animated cartoon, teams of artists _____³ dozens of

drawings which are then _____⁴ on a 'storyboard'. A digital camera linked to

a computer _____⁵ them in the

story's correct order. For recording, each drawing

is _____⁶ under a sheet of

glass to keep it flat and absolutely still. If the

drawings _____⁷ slightly, the

film's characters will _____⁸

around jerkily on the screen. The computer then

_____⁹ each moving sequence of

drawings to see that a horse _____¹⁰

correctly or a hero's walking action looks natural.

In recent years, some artists have preferred to _____¹¹ human characters

instead of the cartoon animals _____¹² by Walt Disney's 'storymen'. Recent

films like Stuart Little have _____¹³ real-life actors and computer-animated

characters which almost look real. It is thought that, in future, computer animations more

life-like than Stuart Little may _____¹⁴ some screen roles from real actors to

avoid the huge salaries _____¹⁵ to film stars.

Use the following words to complete the passage.

young   dangerous   spinning   countries   dangers   today   ignore
swallowed   costs   Christmas   injury   cartwheels   kites   film   batteries

Children's Toys

Ancient Greek and Roman children flew their [_____]¹, rolled hoops and

whipped tops, but didn't have the variety of toys you have [_____]².

Many very expensive toys appear around [_____]³. However, the top toy in

pre-Christmas sales in 2002 was a simple [_____]⁴ top called a 'beyblade'. It

is used to play 'attack' games and only [_____]⁵ about £6.

Toys are great fun but there are also

[_____]⁶. Messages on

some packets warn that a particular toy

may be [_____]⁷ for

children under three as it contains tiny

parts which could be [_____]⁸.

Others may have sharp points which could cause

[_____]⁹ or contain poisonous liquids,

such as are sometimes found in paints or crayons. We must remember that some

[_____]¹⁰ which make toys do not have our strict safety standards. One toy, a

plastic elf based on a character in a Harry Potter [_____]¹¹, has been

described as very dangerous for [_____]¹² children by one member of

Parliament.

Some modern toys are amazing—they can do [_____]¹³, talk to you, and

remind you they are there when you [_____]¹⁴ them! There are plastic balls

with [_____]¹⁵ inside which even bounce around by themselves!

Use the following words to complete the poem. Use the rhyming words to help you fill in the spaces.

site   know   results   display   sign   walls   brains   town
mine   adults   right   trains   show   way   down   scrawls

Graffiti

Annoying tags the world sees on [_____]¹,

Not works of art, but just plain [_____]².

Councils dislike them, they feel they're not [_____]³,

They make efforts to clear them from every [_____]⁴,

Street gangs use them: 'This area's [_____]⁵',

It marks their territory, a warning [_____]⁶.

Tags scratched on windows in buses and [_____]⁷,

Visual pollution by irresponsible [_____]⁸.

Some are fine artists as you and I [_____]⁹,

Decorated bus shelters – their creations on [_____]¹⁰.

They brighten drab walls in poor parts of [_____]¹¹,

With bubble letter messages written [_____]¹².

Chemical blasts wipe off a [_____]¹³,

By selfish taggers who go their own [_____]¹⁴.

Shopkeepers' spray cans sold only to [_____]¹⁵,

We're battling graffiti and getting [_____]¹⁶.

fossils   size   found   dinosaur   mystery   century   elephant   skeleton
hunted   foothills   scientists   unsolved   million   plains   every

Dinosaurs

Dinosaurs were amazing creatures. Some were plant-eaters while others were meat-eaters.

Some were the [_____]¹ of a chicken! Others were many times bigger than an

[_____]² but with a brain the same size as your pet cat's! They lived millions

of years ago, but [_____]³ discover several new kinds of dinosaur fossil

[_____]⁴ year. Discoveries are mainly made in China, Mongolia, the central

[_____]⁵ of the USA, Argentina and Australia.

At the start of this [_____]⁶, two

fossils were discovered in China. They were

about 130 [_____]⁷ years old.

One is the first to be [_____]⁸

with its feather-like body covering still

intact.

Recently, researchers in the [_____]⁹

of the Andes Mountains found the almost complete

[_____]¹⁰ of a meat-eater. It is possibly the world's oldest [_____]¹¹

fossil—230 million years old! (It would take you 11 days to count to one million!) The same

expedition also found [_____]¹² of two predators near a river. They had a bird-like

skull and [_____]¹³ their prey standing upright on two hind legs.

We know a lot about them—but the [_____]¹⁴ of why dinosaurs disappeared

still remains [_____]¹⁵.

Use the following words to complete the passage.

clear	screens	thumbprint	animal	wood	boring	skin	change
darkens	most	kinds	future	walls	outside	panes	

Homes of the Future

Class 4H

All Saints Primary School

Dear Stephanie,

In your letter you mentioned what you are studying at school.

We're studying different [_____]¹ *of homes—mud-brick houses, Indian tepees*

made from [_____]² *hides, Inuit igloos built of ice, and American pioneer*

cabins. But our teacher says the homes of the [_____]³ *will amaze us all!*

We've all heard about huge plasma TV [_____]⁴ *we'll have hanging on the*

[_____]⁵*, but what about walls made from soy flour and recycled newspaper! This*

is a product called 'Environ' which looks like granite but can be drilled, hammered and sawn

like [_____]⁶*. And there's a paint being developed for outside walls that can*

[_____]⁷ *colour! When the weather is cold the paint* [_____]⁸

to absorb more heat. (Remember that T-shirt you had that changed colour when you got hot?)

How about windows that go [_____]⁹ *at the flick of a switch! 'Viracon' uses liquid*

crystals (the stuff used in watch screens), sandwiching them between [_____]¹⁰

of glass to make it look foggy. When electricity is passed through, the liquid crystals go clear

and, hey presto, you can see [_____]¹¹*! Amazing!*

But that's not the [_____]¹² *amazing thing Mr Harris said. We'll have a mirror with*

a camera and LCD screen that can check our health by analysing [_____]¹³ *colour!*

Electronic diaries that will scan a [_____]¹⁴ *to open doors to cars and homes*

seemed [_____]¹⁵ *after this!*

Kate

Use the following NOUNS to complete the passage.

angelfish	hive	legs	tigers	cockroach	Patterns	leopards	ground
snowflake	animals	stripes	butterfly	numbers	scientists	speeds	

Patterns and Numbers in Nature

_____¹ are found everywhere in nature. We have the pattern of hexagonal

shapes on a honeycomb in a bees' _____² and the rhomboid shapes on a

snake's scales. There is also the six-sided rotation symmetry of an icy _____³.

Left and right symmetry is common. The right wing of a beautiful _____⁴ is

the mirror image of the left one and other insects are the same.

Parallel stripes are seen on

_____⁵ and zebras

but jaguars, cheetahs and

_____⁶ have

spots. Fish also have stripes and

Japanese _____⁷

have shown that horizontal

stripe patterns on the tropical

_____⁸ break apart and

then rejoin. New _____⁹

develop as the fish grows.

Numbers are found too. When a _____¹⁰ moves fast it uses two sets of three

legs. The front and back left _____¹¹ move with the middle right leg and vice

versa. When centipedes travel at high _____¹² sometimes only three legs out of

40 touch the _____¹³ at one time! Amoeba, tiny _____¹⁴ with

only one cell, certainly know their _____¹⁵. They multiply by dividing!

cars   run   friends   grandparents   kilometres   records   race   motorways

sausages   people   school   towns   hour   seconds   destination

Speed!

Your [_____]¹ probably tell you that life is just too fast for them today. They

think too many [_____]² want to live their lives at breakneck speed. High-

speed [_____]³ have been built all around the world so people can reach

their [_____]⁴ more quickly

at speeds of at least 100 km per

[_____]⁵. That's

much faster than the early

steam [_____]⁶

in Britain. They could only

travel at 3 km per hour in

[_____]⁷

because of a law passed in

1865. It was quicker to walk!

And what about some of the speed

[_____]⁸ listed in the 2003 Guinness Book of Records? They include the fastest

backwards [_____]⁹ from Los Angeles to New York—a distance of 2 400

[_____]¹⁰! Another entry tells us that a New Zealander ate eight

[_____]¹¹ in just one minute. Perhaps you and one of your

[_____]¹² could beat the book's listed record of nine [_____]¹³

for a 50-metre, three-legged [_____]¹⁴ achieved by the pupils of a Japanese

[_____]¹⁵. It's worth a try!

Games Around the World

Papago

stone

sand

For thousands of years many of the world's children have played

_____¹ which help to improve their physical and

mental skills.

Moteca

stones   buttons

Children in the Dominican Republic play

'_____²' and use a spinning top to try to knock

_____³ off small stones. The stones are placed in

a _____⁴ drawn on the ground. Inuit children spin a top inside their home

and try to run _____⁵ the house before it stops spinning!

Nigerian youngsters play a war _____⁶ game. Team

Haba Gaba

3
2
1

members sit on a _____⁷ and move backwards

across a 'river' drawn on the ground. A _____⁸

steers them around obstacles representing rocks, crocodiles etc.

'Haba Gaba' is a game played in Sierra Leone in _____⁹,

with each player given three throws and the highest score winning.

'Papago' is a native American Indian game using _____¹⁰ paper cups. They

are filled with sand. One has a _____¹¹ hidden in it.

War canoe

If player 1 finds it at his/her first _____¹², he/she

earns four points. His/Her second try earns three points and so on.

The first player to reach 10 points _____¹³ the game.

At Easter, Dutch children gently bump hard-boiled _____¹⁴

together. The person whose egg is the _____¹⁵ to crack is the winner!

Use the following words to complete the passage. Look at the map and bar graph to fill some spaces.

northern **warm** **Russia** **four** **children** **bite** **harmless** **year**
century **disease** **Australia** **Africa** **drugs** **Korea** **scientists**

Fighting Malaria

Malaria is a disease found in [_____]¹ humid climates. It is spread by a

[_____]² from the female Anopheles mosquito. Millions of people die each

year; most are [_____]³ under the age of 10.

Control of the [_____]⁴ has become

more difficult as it has developed a resistance to

some of the [_____]⁵ used by doctors.

However, in the 21st [_____]⁶

experts expect to find a cure. In 2002,

[_____]⁷ discovered the mosquito's

gene pattern. They now hope to make the insect

[_____]⁸ by experimenting with those genes.

World Malaria Areas

Russia

Canada

USA

Africa

PNG

South
America

Australia

Malaria Cases: Asia-Pacific Region: 2000

Cambodia
China
Laos
Malaysia
Philippines
Papua New Guinea
Korea
Solomon Isles
Vanuatu
Vietnam

0 10 20 30 40 50 60 70 80 90 100
Thousands

In the [_____]⁹ hemisphere,

America, Canada and [_____]¹⁰ are

free of malaria, but people in [_____]¹¹,

India and South America suffer a great deal. The

graph of the Asia-Pacific region shows most cases

in the [_____]¹² 2000 were found in

Papua New Guinea, which lies just north of

[_____]¹³. Of the countries listed, only [_____]¹⁴ had fewer

than 20 000 cases, and [_____]¹⁵ had about the same number as Vanuatu.

dollars	tadpoles	getting	South	hunt	spread	foxes	lay
painful	suburbs	farmers	poisoned	sugar	destroying	damage	

Nature Fights Back

Many animals are endangered or extinct because we [_____]¹ them or destroy their environment. Perhaps now they're [_____]² their own back!

Cane toads were brought to Queensland in Australia to control [_____]³ cane beetles. They've increased to huge numbers as they can [_____]⁴ up to 10 000 eggs at a time. They are spreading across north Australia, eating native [_____]⁵ and lizards. Even pets can be [_____]⁶ if they eat these toads!

This century, South American fire ants have [_____]⁷ northwards across some States in the USA. They have a [_____]⁸ bite and cost America millions of [_____]⁹ each year. Their nest mounds are so hard they damage farm machinery, so [_____]¹⁰ are very unhappy. Now these ants have been found in Australia.

Argentine ants, also from [_____]¹¹ America, were recently found in New Zealand. They [_____]¹² fruit crops and climb trees, sometimes killing baby native birds.

Bears in Canada and [_____]¹³ in Britain are often found scavenging food from rubbish bins in city [_____]¹⁴. Thousands of crown-of-thorns starfish are slowly [_____]¹⁵ some of the world's finest reefs. Looks like nature's fighting back!

Use the following ADJECTIVES to complete the passage.

harmful   valuable   special   enormous   reusable   several   red   brilliant
thrilling   outer   new   important   far-off   regular   different

Space Travel

Space travel has fascinated the world's [_____]¹ scientists for years. Since the moon landings, the [_____]² targets have been Venus and the '[_____]³ planet', Mars—which are both closer to Earth than the other planets.

A [_____]⁴ camera on the 'Odyssey' spacecraft has been photographing the surface of Mars and the 'Cassini' probe will orbit [_____]⁵ Saturn in the near future. The 'Stardust' spacecraft is at present collecting dust from a comet's tail in [_____]⁶ space and will return [_____]⁷ information to Earth several years from now.

Rocket planes can fly over 7000 km/h and [_____]⁸ space flights are expected during the 21st century. The price of one ticket on 'Xerus', a rocket plane planned to take tourists on a [_____]⁹ one-hour trial flight in the next decade, is £105 000!

Astronauts from [_____]¹⁰ countries have spent months orbiting in space to test possible [_____]¹¹ effects. These experiments will lead to space stations where people will live and work for [_____]¹² years.

If space travel for ordinary people is to become a reality, the scientists need to cut the [_____]¹³ costs. At present, a shuttle's main fuel tank drops away in flight and must be replaced for each [_____]¹⁴ mission. One way to reduce this huge expense is to develop [_____]¹⁵ launch vehicles, and various designs are being tested.

Use the following words to complete the passage.

something   lazy   England   changing   called   adults   centuries

years   plane   different   word   young   shorten   pupils   Roman

Our Changing Language

There are thousands of languages and over the _____ [1] our English language has seen many changes. An Old English _____ [2] like 'cese' has become 'cheese' and 'forca' is now 'fork'. The Saxon invaders of _____ [3] called short garments 'shirts', whereas the Danes, also invaders, _____ [4] them 'skirts'. Now, centuries later, they mean totally _____ [5] articles of clothing!

Humans tend to be _____ [6] so refrigerator, omnibus, aeroplane and telephone have become fridge, bus, _____ [7] and phone. Even Shakespeare shortened 'do not' to 'don't'—and that was over 300 _____ [8] ago! Our words 'autumn' and 'hymn' were once ancient _____ [9] words 'autumnus' and 'hymnus' but, hey, let's _____ [10] them!

Nowadays, _____ [11] people are _____ [12] our language. Who'd have thought that _____ [13] you did that was 'wicked' was good! A wicked witch—a good one? 'Gross' can mean 144 items to _____ [14], but 'yuck' to their children. Let's hope the _____ [15] reading this think it's 'cool'!

Use the following ADJECTIVES to complete the passage.

staring   young   clever   overweight   serious   Long   painful   short   unsuitable
English   unfortunate   comfortable   developing   America   suitable

Computers and Your Health

An [_____]¹ expert warns that most computers are designed for adults. He

says [_____]² children using them can damage their health. A child's

[_____]³ muscles and bones could be harmed and [_____]⁴

neck and bone problems follow in later life. Recent research in [_____]⁵ and

England shows many school pupils suffer frequent neck and back pain. As a result,

[_____]⁶ designers are being asked

to design [_____]⁷

computers for children.

Japanese experts have found we

shouldn't be [_____]⁸

at computer screens for hour after

hour. They reported that

[_____]⁹ headaches

and eyestrain were problems for those

[_____]¹⁰ or foolish enough to

spend over five hours a day in front of a computer. [_____]¹¹ periods sitting down

are also thought to be one reason we see so many [_____]¹² children. Another

study found many schools had [_____]¹³ chairs and tables which couldn't be

raised or lowered for different age groups.

REMEMBER! Position the chair and keyboard so you are [_____]¹⁴, rest your

feet flat on the floor and take frequent [_____]¹⁵ breaks.

Use the following NOUNS to complete the passage.

horse   pottery   pictures   doctors   suits   Statue   bodies   signals
metals   dolphins   friction   Sweden   problems   paint   children

Benefits from Space Research

The enormous pressures on astronauts' [   ][1] *at lift-off led to a new foam*

material made in [   ][2]. *It spreads pressure around the body as a person*

sleeps and now [   ][3] *recommend mattresses made of it.*

Superman star, Christopher Reeve, was paralysed when he fell from a [   ][4].

He now uses a space research invention which sends tiny electrical [   ][5]

to stimulate muscles and nerves and maintain his fitness.

Christopher Reeve

NASA technology, which took amazing

[   ][6] *of the moon, is now used*

for eye testing. Young [   ][7]

don't sit still long enough for normal tests but

now thousands are screened to detect possible

future [   ][8].

Insulating materials made from [   ][9] *and ceramics protected the space*

shuttles from the fierce heat caused by [   ][10] *as they re-entered Earth's*

atmosphere. These materials are now used in firefighters' [   ][11].

Space research has led to many benefits: sensors which help archaeologists to find ancient

[   ][12] *buried underground and 'bleepers' attached to underwater nets to*

prevent [   ][13] *becoming entangled. A ceramic* [   ][14] *used*

to protect the Apollo launching pad now protects bridges and the [   ][15] *of*

Liberty from corrosion!

The Book or the Film?

Would Hans Christian Andersen, who [_____]¹ The Little Mermaid *around* 1836, like the Walt Disney [_____]² *better than his book? Perhaps he would,* with [_____]³ *the wonderful computer images used in modern* [_____]⁴!

Some children prefer the book as they can [_____]⁵ *it at their own* speed. Others are disappointed when so many [_____]⁶ *of the* story are omitted by film makers. One [_____]⁷ *in a recent* survey was very annoyed when she found details about a troll and a trapdoor had been [_____]⁸ *out of a Harry Potter film.* Many young [_____]⁹ *preferred to read the book* [_____]¹⁰ they saw the film. They thought that watching the film [_____]¹¹ *took away*

some of the interest and excitement. A number of children liked to [_____]¹² *the various* characters in their [_____]¹³ using the more detailed descriptions usually found in [_____]¹⁴. *Also, it* costs you absolutely nothing to borrow a book from a public [_____]¹⁵.

Which do you prefer?

Use the following words to complete the passage. Look at the map to fill some of the spaces.

skins   protect   Bwindi   surface   find   Santiago   underground   China
breeding   elephants   medicines   Kenya   Java   diseases   Madrid

Endangered Animal Snippets

An Australian wildlife conservation group was formed in 2001 to [_____]¹ 50

endangered native mammals. In November 2002, officials from 160 countries met in

[_____]², Chile's capital, to discuss trade in endangered species. Outside,

hundreds of students protested that [_____]³ would suffer if ivory trading

bans were lifted.

In Asia, 'jinbou' is the ancient belief that

[_____]⁴ made from animal

parts improve poor health. One result is that

tiger [_____]⁵ in homes are

more common than tigers in the wild! In

2002, in [_____]⁶, Spain's capital,

the city's zoo was trying to [_____]⁷ a

mate for its Iberian lynx. With fewer than 200 left, they hope to start a [_____]⁸

programme. There are fewer than 100 of the world's only [_____]⁹

elephants who move into caves at night in [_____]¹⁰, Africa. The silvery gibbons

native to the island of [_____]¹¹ in Indonesia are seriously threatened. Concerned

scientists fear that human [_____]¹² from tourists may reduce mountain

gorilla numbers in Uganda's [_____]¹³ National Park. The number of pandas in

a nature reserve in Sichuan province in [_____]¹⁴ is also declining.

Only 5% of the Earth's [_____]¹⁵ is protected for wildlife. Let's hope that this

area is greatly expanded in the 21st century.

The Water Cycle

The [_____]¹ cycle is part of our daily lives. Clouds produce rain which falls

onto land areas, [_____]², lakes and rivers. Most of the rain which falls on to

the [_____]³ is evaporated by the sun's heat or flows underground into the

Earth's waterways. Water from a [_____]⁴ or lake can be purified in a water

[_____]⁵ works. This clean water is used in factories and [_____]⁶

and then [_____]⁷

carry the waste water from

these buildings to a

[_____]⁸

treatment plant. Any

unused treated water

is then returned to the

[_____]⁹

and rivers where the cycle

begins again.

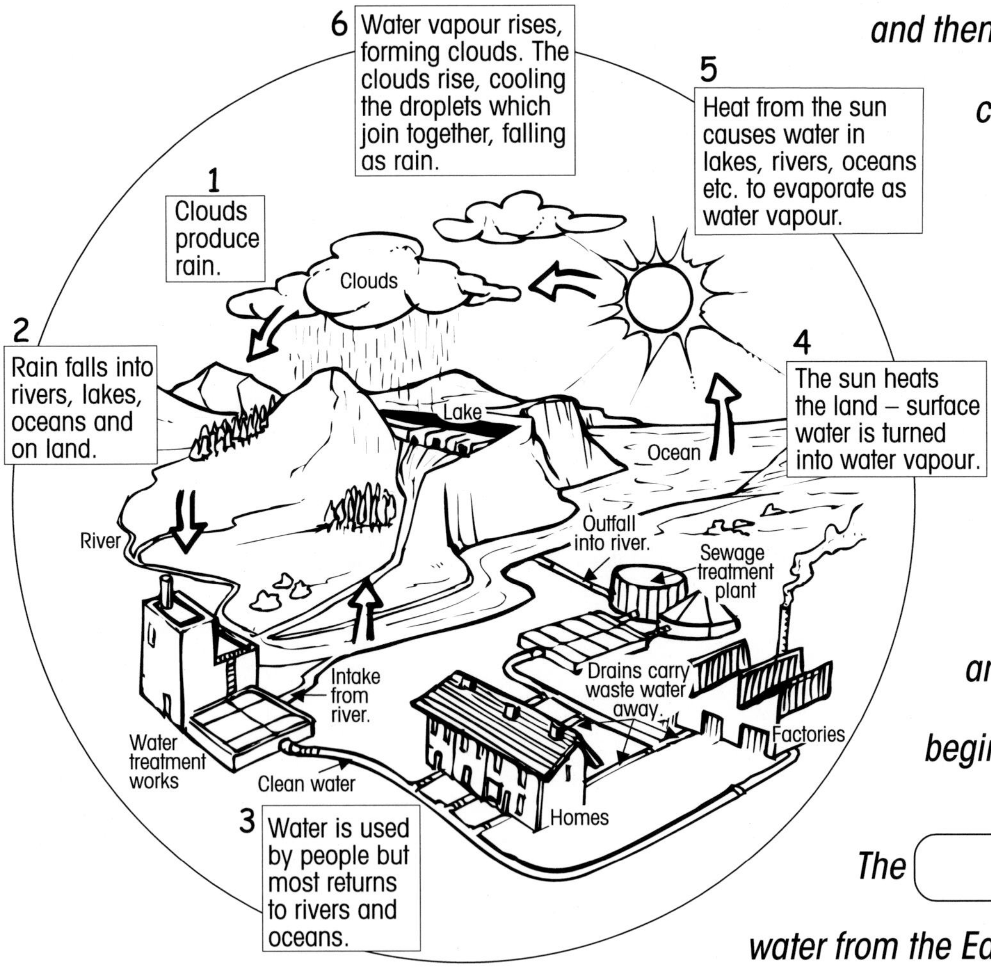

The [_____]¹⁰ evaporates

water from the Earth's surface and from

the leaves of plants. This invisible water [_____]¹¹ rises and cools into tiny

water droplets which form [_____]¹². As the clouds rise higher the water

vapour cools even more and the drops join together to form bigger drops of water. These

[_____]¹³ become too heavy to stay in the air, so they fall as

[_____]¹⁴. The sun heats the water and the [_____]¹⁵ begins again.

Diagram labels:

6 Water vapour rises, forming clouds. The clouds rise, cooling the droplets which join together, falling as rain.

5 Heat from the sun causes water in lakes, rivers, oceans etc. to evaporate as water vapour.

1 Clouds produce rain.

Clouds

2 Rain falls into rivers, lakes, oceans and on land.

4 The sun heats the land – surface water is turned into water vapour.

Lake

Ocean

River

Outfall into river.

Sewage treatment plant

Intake from river.

Drains carry waste water away.

Factories

Water treatment works

Clean water

Homes

3 Water is used by people but most returns to rivers and oceans.

Use the following words to complete the passage. Use the illustrations to fill some of the spaces.

duck   cashew   hot   French   lime   citizens   sweet   make

grandparents   rolls   millions   diners   recipes   enjoy   elsewhere

Multicultural Foods

For many years, [_____]¹ of people have moved from their own countries to seek a better life [_____]². With them they took their traditional [_____]³ which they introduced to generations of [_____]⁴ in their new homeland.

We now have restaurants which serve us [_____]⁵ dishes with frogs' legs! Chinese restaurants have their sliced [_____]⁶ with bean sprouts and ginger. Families around the country eat takeaway Thai meals flavoured with [_____]⁷ leaves, coconut milk and [_____]⁸ nuts. Indian migrants have brought spicy meat dishes with delicious [_____]⁹ sauces. Vietnamese vegetarian spring [_____]¹⁰ dipped in a tasty thin sauce are also very popular with diners. Plus everyone loves baklavas, [_____]¹¹ Greek pastries made with honey and nuts!

These exotic foods [_____]¹² the potatoes, roast meat and vegetables eaten by your [_____]¹³ sound very ordinary, don't they? I'm sure we all [_____]¹⁴ these tasty foods brought by our new [_____]¹⁵.

Use the following NOUNS to complete the passage.

awards   Horse   author   worked   wizard   films   books   booksellers
Myrtle   names   languages   child   truancy   schools   France

The Harry Potter Phenomenon

Joanne Kathleen Rowling is the [_____]1 of the popular books about an

orphan Harry Potter, who is a young [_____]2. The author was born in England

and says as a [_____]3 she 'lived in a fantasy world'. Her favourite book, 'The

Little White [_____]4', influenced

the Harry Potter series of seven planned

books. Rowling taught English in

[_____]5 and Portugal

and also [_____]6 for

Amnesty International.

Her [_____]7 have

been praised by reviewers throughout

Europe and have won many European

book [_____]8. They have

been translated into more than 28

[_____]9, sold in more than 130 countries and made into [_____]10

which are exciting and very, very popular.

Children love the interesting character [_____]11 like Helga Hufflepuff,

Moaning [_____]12 and Nearly Headless Nick. Book sales have been huge but

some church [_____]13 have banned them because of their emphasis on

witchcraft. When [_____]14 released the third book in Britain, they were asked

to sell them after school hours so that [_____]15 wouldn't be a problem!

Use the following words to complete the passage. Use information from the graph to fill some spaces.

nations   preserved   minke   islands   windiest   oil   penguins   protests
size   harmful   southern   declare   blue   ships   largest

Antarctica

Antarctica is 14 million square kilometres in area, the coldest and one of the [_____]¹ regions on Earth. Its waters teem with life like the [_____]² whales, which reach 10 m in length. This is one-third the size of the [_____]³ whale. Unfortunately, whalers killed over 400 minke whales in 2001 despite [_____]⁴ from around the world.

The environmental group Greenpeace believes Antarctica should be [_____]⁵ as a world park. It thinks its wildlife, like leopard seals, the [_____]⁶ elephant seals and the emperor [_____]⁷, should be protected for future generations. Greenpeace [_____]⁸ regularly visit the region to interfere with whaling fleets or check on possible [_____]⁹ developments in this unique environment. It realises that several [_____]¹⁰ are interested in the area as it may hold huge deposits of [_____]¹¹ and minerals.

The Australian Heard and McDonald [_____]¹² form part of the Antarctic region. By early 2003, Australia will [_____]¹³ them part of the world's latest and [_____]¹⁴ marine park. It will be 6.5 million hectares in area, almost the [_____]¹⁵ of Switzerland!

Antarctic Creatures – Approx. Sizes

Creature	Metres
Humpback whale	(bar to ~18)
Blue whale	(bar to ~30)
Emperor penguin	(bar to ~1)
Minke whale	(bar to ~10)
Leopard whale	(bar to ~3)
Killer whale	(bar to ~8)
Southern elephant seal	(bar to ~5)
Sperm whale	(bar to ~16)

0 5 10 15 20 25 30 35
Metres

Astronauts

Explorers have [_____]¹ on unknown waters, trekked across hot deserts under

a burning [_____]² or cut their way through dense jungles. There are also

courageous astronauts who risk their [_____]³ as they explore outer space.

Chinese astronauts have to be [_____]⁴ than 45, but former American

astronaut John Glenn, a US senator, was 77 years [_____]⁵ when he last flew in

space! The American astronauts have no age limit but

need to be very [_____]⁶ to pass

extremely strict physical [_____]⁷.

New entrants are [_____]⁸ by

top scientists and experienced astronauts who

make them aware of the [_____]⁹

they will face in space. These problems include

cramped living [_____]¹⁰, radiation

storms, space debris, zero gravity (weightlessness), motion sickness and [_____]¹¹

eye-hand coordination. Astronauts also have to [_____]¹² freeze-dried food, but

experiments to produce an onboard ecosystem by scientists in Germany could see astronauts

eating fresh fish in the near [_____]¹³.

[_____]¹⁴ have also taken huge risks in space. Russian cosmonaut Valentina

Tereshkova was the [_____]¹⁵ woman in space and American Eileen Collins the

first to command a space shuttle.

Do you have what it takes to be an astronaut in the 21st century?

Answers

Bicycles! Bicycles! Bicycles!

Page 1

1. holiday
2. three
3. America
4. Japan
5. popular
6. gifts
7. school
8. accidents
9. crowded
10. roads
11. barriers
12. cars
13. factories
14. year
15. copied

Raising Healthy Children

Page 2

1. spend
2. means
3. doubled
4. helps
5. improves
6. warned
7. showed
8. choose
9. work
10. include
11. Keep
12. builds
13. stay
14. wash
15. visit

Strange Creatures

Page 3

1. microscopes
2. seen
3. swimming
4. angler
5. teeth
6. catch
7. Africa
8. dancing
9. ants
10. fruit
11. tongue
12. hide
13. mammal
14. appearance
15. creatures

Sun Safety

Page 4

1. tan
2. can
3. thin
4. skin
5. delay
6. play
7. plus
8. fuss
9. school
10. rule
11. midday
12. grey
13. checks
14. sex
15. aware

Animated Films

Page 5

1. began
2. painted
3. complete
4. displayed
5. records
6. placed
7. move
8. jump
9. checks
10. gallops
11. use
12. drawn
13. mixed
14. take
15. paid

Children's Toys

Page 6

1. kites
2. today
3. Christmas
4. spinning
5. costs
6. dangers
7. dangerous
8. swallowed
9. injury
10. countries
11. film
12. young
13. cartwheels
14. ignore
15. batteries

Graffiti

Page 7

1. walls
2. scrawls
3. right
4. site
5. mine
6. sign
7. trains
8. brains
9. know
10. show
11. town
12. down
13. display
14. way
15. adults
16. results

Dinosaurs

Page 8

1. size
2. elephant
3. scientists
4. every
5. plains
6. century
7. million
8. found
9. foothills
10. skeleton
11. dinosaur
12. fossils
13. hunted
14. mystery
15. unsolved

Homes of the Future

Page 9

1. kinds
2. animal
3. future
4. screens
5. walls
6. wood
7. change
8. darkens
9. clear
10. panes
11. outside
12. most
13. skin
14. thumbprint
15. boring

Patterns and Numbers in Nature

Page 10

1. Patterns
2. hive
3. snowflake
4. butterfly
5. tigers
6. leopards
7. scientists
8. angelfish
9. stripes
10. cockroach
11. legs
12. speeds
13. ground
14. animals
15. numbers

Speed!

Page 11

1. grandparents
2. people
3. motorways
4. destination
5. hour
6. cars
7. towns
8. records
9. run
10. kilometres
11. sausages
12. friends
13. seconds
14. race
15. school

Games Around the World

Page 12

1. games
2. Moteca
3. buttons
4. circle
5. round
6. canoe
7. pole
8. guide
9. Africa
10. four
11. stone
12. attempt/try
13. wins
14. eggs
15. last

Fighting Malaria

Page 13

1. warm
2. bite
3. children
4. disease
5. drugs
6. century
7. scientists
8. harmless
9. northern
10. Russia
11. Africa
12. year
13. Australia
14. four
15. Korea

Nature Fights Back

Page 14

1. hunt
2. getting
3. sugar
4. lay
5. tadpoles
6. poisoned
7. spread
8. painful
9. dollars
10. farmers
11. South
12. damage
13. foxes
14. suburbs
15. destroying

Space Travel

Page 15

1. brilliant
2. important
3. red
4. special
5. far-off
6. outer
7. valuable
8. regular
9. thrilling
10. different
11. harmful
12. several
13. enormous
14. new
15. reusable

Answers

Our Changing Language
Page 16

1. centuries
2. word
3. England
4. called
5. different
6. lazy
7. plane
8. years
9. Roman
10. shorten
11. young
12. changing
13. something
14. adults
15. pupils

Computers and Your Health
Page 17

1. English
2. young
3. developing
4. serious
5. America
6. clever
7. suitable
8. staring
9. painful
10. unfortunate
11. Long
12. overweight
13. unsuitable
14. comfortable
15. short

Benefits from Space Research
Page 18

1. bodies
2. Sweden
3. doctors
4. horse
5. signals
6. pictures
7. children
8. problems
9. metals
10. friction
11. suits
12. pottery
13. dolphins
14. paint
15. Statue

The Book or the Film?
Page 19

1. wrote
2. film
3. all
4. films
5. read
6. details/parts
7. girl/boy/child
8. left
9. readers/children
10. before
11. first
12. visualise/imagine/picture
13. minds/heads
14. books
15. library

Endangered Animal Snippets
Page 20

1. protect
2. Santiago
3. elephants
4. medicines
5. skins
6. Madrid
7. find
8. breeding
9. underground
10. Kenya
11. Java
12. diseases
13. Bwindi
14. China
15. surface

The Water Cycle
Page 21

1. water
2. oceans
3. land
4. river
5. treatment
6. homes
7. drains
8. sewage
9. ocean
10. sun
11. vapour
12. clouds
13. drops
14. rain
15. cycle

Multicultural Foods
Page 22

1. millions
2. elsewhere
3. recipes
4. diners
5. French
6. duck
7. lime
8. cashew
9. hot
10. rolls
11. sweet
12. make
13. grandparents
14. enjoy
15. citizens

The Harry Potter Phenomenon
Page 23

1. author
2. wizard
3. child
4. Horse
5. France
6. worked
7. books
8. awards
9. languages
10. films
11. names
12. Myrtle
13. schools
14. booksellers
15. truancy

Antarctica
Page 24

1. windiest
2. minke
3. blue
4. protests
5. preserved
6. southern
7. penguins
8. ships
9. harmful
10. nations
11. oil
12. islands
13. declare
14. largest
15. size

Astronauts
Page 25

1. sailed
2. sun
3. lives
4. younger
5. old
6. fit
7. examinations/tests
8. taught/trained
9. problems
10. quarters/areas
11. poor
12. eat
13. future
14. Women
15. first